The Story of Christmas

By Paul Fehlner
Illustrated by Kathy Mitchell

A GOLDEN BOOK • NEW YORK
Western Publishing Company, Inc., Racine, Wisconsin 53404

Many years ago, in the land of Judah, there was a time of great trouble. The people lived under a harsh Roman emperor, Caesar Augustus, and an evil king named Herod. Under their rule, the people of Judah were poor and miserable.

But the people were also filled with hope, because God had promised to send them a savior. This savior would bring them joy and peace.

In the town of Nazareth there lived a young woman named Mary. Mary was kind and gentle. Like the other women of Nazareth, Mary led a simple life.

Then one day God sent the angel Gabriel to Mary. "The Lord is with you," Gabriel said to Mary.

Mary was troubled by Gabriel's visit, and she wondered why he had come to her. But Gabriel said, "Fear not, Mary. I come with glad tidings. You shall give birth to a son, and you shall call him Jesus. This baby shall be the Savior, the Son of God."

Mary bowed her head. "I am ready to serve God," she said.

Mary was to be married to a carpenter named Joseph. In a dream, God sent an angel to tell Joseph about the coming of the Savior.

"I bring you tidings of great joy," said the angel. "Mary shall be the mother of God's Son."

Joseph was filled with happiness, and he and Mary became husband and wife.

At this time a command went out from the emperor in Rome. It said that all people should return to the city of their birth to be taxed.

Joseph was born in Bethlehem, so he had to travel there from Nazareth. Although Mary was soon to give birth, she went with him.

Joseph and Mary began their journey to Bethlehem.
They traveled for many days over high mountains and rough
roads. When they finally arrived in Bethlehem, Mary and
Joseph found that many other people had come to be taxed.
  Joseph went from house to house, seeking shelter for the
night. But there was no room for them. At each place
Joseph and Mary were turned away.

Finally Joseph and Mary came to an inn where the kind host offered them the only room he had—a place in his stable.

It was in that stable that the baby Jesus was born.
Mary wrapped the child in swaddling clothes and laid
him down.

Outside Bethlehem shepherds were in the fields, keeping watch over their flocks. Suddenly an angel of God appeared before them. The shepherds fell to the ground, for they were filled with fear.

The angel said, "Do not be afraid. I bring you news of a great joy that comes to all people: A Savior is born this day in Bethlehem who is Christ the Lord. And this shall be a sign to you: You shall find a babe wrapped in swaddling clothes, lying in a manger."

And all at once the sky was filled with angels who praised God, saying, "Glory to God in the highest, and on Earth peace and goodwill to all people."

The shepherds said to one another, "Let us go to Bethlehem and see this wondrous thing that the Lord has made known to us."

So they hurried to Bethlehem. There they saw the baby Jesus, wrapped in swaddling clothes, lying in a manger, just as the angel had said.

The shepherds told Mary and Joseph what the angel had told them. After they gave thanks, the shepherds rushed to tell the people of Bethlehem the wonderful news—Christ the Lord was born!

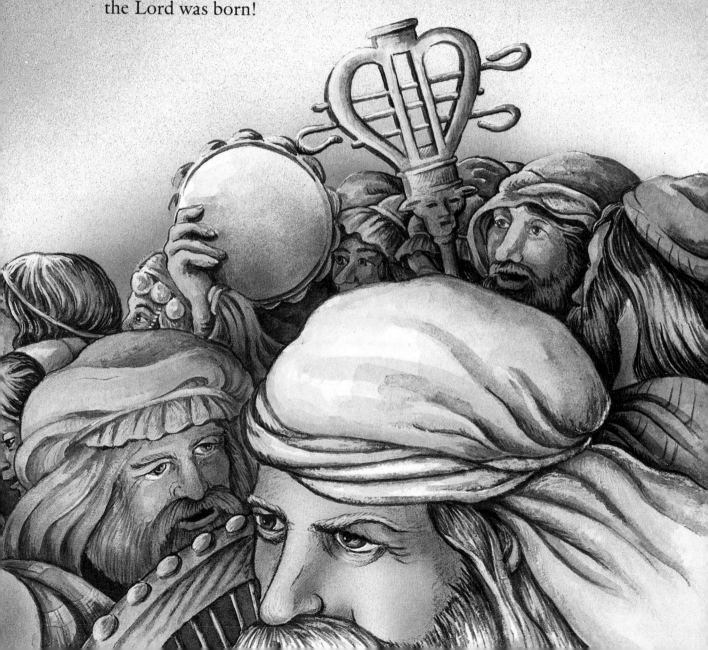

Faraway in the East three wise men saw a brilliant star rising in the sky. They rejoiced, for they knew that the star was a sign that the Savior had been born. The wise men, bearing precious gifts, followed the star to the stable in Bethlehem.

The three wise men walked toward the manger where Jesus lay. They fell to the floor and worshipped him. Then, opening their treasures, they offered gifts of gold, frankincense, and myrrh.

Many others had come to worship the newborn king as
well. As the people gathered around the baby they gave
thanks to God for sending them his Son.